Rory the Tea-Rex

By **Clare Helen Welsh**

Illustrated by
Claudio Cerri

When Rory the Tea-Rex arrived in town, the other animals did not trust her.

Rory had sharp claws and huge teeth.

She had a big suitcase too.

"What's inside it?" the animals whispered.

The animals needed to know,

so they decided to spy on Rory.

They saw her sharpening her claws.

"Eek! She's going to catch us!" the

animals said.

Next, they saw Rory unpacking cooking equipment and lighting a flame.

"She's going to catch and cook us!"

the animals said.

Then the animals saw a huge pile of cutlery and plates.

"She's going to catch us and cook us,

then **eat** us!" they screamed.

So, when Rory invited the animals to her house...

...they all said,

"NO WAY!"

16

"It's a trick and we won't fall for it!"

they decided.

The animals waited...

...and waited...

Then, they peered into Rory's garden.

"Ha! She didn't fool us, did she?"

the animals grinned.

"OH!"

The garden was decorated with bunting and flowers. There were cakes and drinks and plates of food.

Rory was sat on a chair all on her own.

A tear rolled down her cheek.

The animals had made a very big mistake.
They felt bad.

"Rory has sharp claws and huge teeth,
but she wasn't going to catch us or
cook us or eat us," they said.
"It really **was** a party!"

27

The animals apologised by inviting

Rory to a special tea party.

"I love tea parties!" she smiled.

"How did you know?"

Quiz

1. What were Rory's teeth like?
a) Sharp
b) Small
c) Huge

2. What was Rory unpacking in her kitchen?
a) Clothes
b) Cooking equipment
c) Presents

3. What did the animals think Rory was going to do to them?
a) Eat them
b) Tickle them
c) Chase them

4. Why did Rory invite the animals to her house?
a) To catch them
b) For a tea party
c) For a disco dance

5. The animals apologised by...
a) sending Rory flowers
b) singing Rory a song
c) inviting Rory to a tea party

Turn over for answers

Book Bands for Guided Reading

The Institute of Education book banding system is a scale of colours that reflects the various levels of reading difficulty. The bands are assigned by taking into account the content, the language style, the layout and phonics. Word, phrase and sentence level work is also taken into consideration.

Maverick Early Readers are a bright, attractive range of books covering the pink to white bands. All of these books have been book banded for guided reading to the industry standard and edited by a leading educational consultant.

To view the whole Maverick Readers scheme, visit our website at
www.maverickearlyreaders.com

Or scan the QR code above to view our scheme instantly!

Quiz Answers: 1c, 2b, 3a, 4b, 5c